Bond

Assessment Papers

More fifth papers in
Verbal Reasoning

Jane Bayliss

Published in 2007 by:
Nelson Thornes Ltd
Delta Place
27 Bath Road
CHELTENHAM
GL53 7TH
United Kingdom

10 11 12 13 / 10 9 8 7 6 5 4

A catalogue record for this book is available from the British Library

ISBN 978 0 7487 8477 6

Page make-up by Tech Set Ltd

Printed and bound in Croatia by Zrinski

Before you get started

What is Bond?

This book is part of the Bond Assessment Papers series for verbal reasoning, which provides a **thorough and progressive course in verbal reasoning** from ages six to twelve. It builds up verbal reasoning skills from book to book over the course of the series.

Bond's verbal reasoning resources are ideal preparation for the 11+ and other secondary school selection exams.

How does the scope of this book match real exam content?

Verbal Reasoning 11+-12+ Book 1 and Book 2 are the advanced Bond 11+ books. Each paper is **pitched at a level above a typical 11+ exam**, providing greater challenges and stretching skills further. The papers practise a wide range of questions drawn from the four distinct groups of verbal reasoning question types: sorting words, selecting words, anagrams, coded sequences and logic. The papers are fully in line with 11+ and other selective exams for this age group but are designed to practise **a wider variety of skills and question types** than most other practice papers so that children are always challenged to think – and don't get bored repeating the same question type again and again. We believe that variety is the key to effective learning. It helps children 'think on their feet' and cope with the unexpected: it is surprising how often children come out of verbal reasoning exams having met question types they have not seen before.

What does the book contain?

- **10 papers** – each one contains 100 questions.
- **Tutorial links throughout** - ▢ – this icon appears in the margin next to the questions. It indicates links to the relevant section in How to do ... 11+ Verbal Reasoning, our invaluable subject guide that offers explanations and practice for all core question types.
- **Scoring devices** – there are score boxes in the margins and a Progress Chart on page 64. The chart is a visual and motivating way for children to see how they are doing. It also turns the score into a percentage that can help decide what to do next.
- **Next Steps Planner** – advice on what to do after finishing the papers can be found on the inside back cover.
- **Answers** – located in an easily-removed central pull-out section. If you lose your answers, please email cservices@nelsonthornes.com for another copy.

How can you use this book?

One of the great strengths of Bond Assessment Papers is their flexibility. They can be used at home, in school and by tutors to:

- set **timed formal practice** tests – allow about 45 minutes per paper in line with standard 11+ demands. Reduce the suggested time limit by five minutes to practise working at speed

- provide **bite-sized chunks** for regular practice

- **highlight strengths and weaknesses** in the core skills

- identify **individual needs**

- set **homework**

- follow **a complete 11+ preparation strategy** alongside *The Parents' Guide to the 11+* (see below).

It is best to start at the beginning and work through the papers in order. If you are using the book as part of a careful run-in to the 11+, we suggest that you also have two other essential Bond resources close at hand:

How to do … 11+ Verbal Reasoning: the subject guide that explains all the question types practised in this book. Use the cross-reference icons to find the relevant sections.

The Parents' Guide to the 11+: the step-by-step guide to the whole 11+ experience. It clearly explains the 11+ process, provides guidance on how to assess children, helps you to set complete action plans for practice and explains how you can use the *Verbal Reasoning 11+-12+ Book 1* and *Book 2* as part of a strategic run-in to the exam.

See the inside front cover for more details of these books.

What does a score mean and how can it be improved?

It is unfortunately impossible to guarantee that a child will pass the 11+ exam if they achieve a certain score on any practice book or paper. Success on the day depends on a host of factors, including the scores of the other children sitting the test. However, we can give some guidance on what a score indicates and how to improve it.

If children colour in the Progress Chart on page 64, this will give an idea of present performance in percentage terms. The Next Steps Planner inside the back cover will help you to decide what to do next to help a child progress. It is always valuable to go over wrong answers with children. If they are having trouble with any particular question type, follow the tutorial links to *How to do … 11+ Verbal Reasoning* for step-by-step explanations and further practice.

Don't forget the website…!

Visit www.bond11plus.co.uk for lots of advice, information and suggestions on everything to do with Bond, the 11+ and helping children to do their best, and exams.

Paper 1

Look at these groups of words.

A	B	C	D
travel	insects	time	liquids

Choose the correct group for each of the words below. Write in the letter.

1–5 luggage ___   vinegar ___   annual ___   midge ___

paraffin ___   modern ___   passenger ___   lemonade ___

flea ___   century ___

B 1

5

Underline two words, one from each group, that go together to form a new word. The word in the first group always comes first.

B 8

Example   (hand, <u>green</u>, for)   (light, <u>house</u>, sure)

6 (circle, ring, square)   (line, friend, leader)

7 (water, ride, trip)   (tap, fall, over)

8 (ice, snow, fog)   (drop, drip, mist)

9 (bright, dull, light)   (air, room, house)

10 (sea, son, sun)   (rose, rise, risk)

5

Find the letter which will end the first word and start the second word.

B 10

Example   peac (<u>h</u>) ome

11 par (___) ake

12 tal (___) ind

13 far (___) etre

14 kit (___) dge

15 sal (___) ooth

5

Find a word that is similar in meaning to the word in capital letters and that rhymes with the second word.

B 5

Example   CABLE   tyre   <u>wire</u>

16 CORRECT   light   ___ ___ ___

17 EARTH   sound   _____

18 TIMEPIECE   mock   _____

19 HINDER   scamper   _____

20 SHOAL   tool   _____

5

Underline the pair of words most similar in meaning.

Example   come, go   <u>roam, wander</u>   fear, fare

21   horde, mob   blunt, sharp   couple, single

22   gather, scatter   launch, begin   veto, allow

23   squander, save   firm, loose   entice, tempt

24   join, separate   grace, charm   novel, unoriginal

25   cease, begin   engrave, carve   mild, wild

Underline one word in the brackets which is most opposite in meaning to the word in capitals.

Example   WIDE   (broad   vague   long   <u>narrow</u>   motorway)

26   LEVEL   (straight   flat   smooth   uneven   horizontal)

27   FILLED   (empty   full   plenty   stuffed   whole)

28   PLACID   (silent   motionless   active   calm   stationary)

29   WAX   (enlarge   rise   wane   swell   develop)

30   ALLY   (partner   friend   mate   colleague   foe)

Rearrange the muddled letters in capitals to make a proper word. The answer will complete the sentence sensibly.

Example   A BEZAR is an animal with stripes.   <u>ZEBRA</u>

31   The two children AKWELD down the lane.   _____

32   The programme was too CYASR for young children.   _____

33   Luckily, she wasn't EJNRIUD in the accident.   _____

34   Olives grow on RETES.   _____

35   UDEIG means to escort someone.   _____

Find the three-letter word which can be added to the letters in capitals to make a new word. The new word will complete the sentence sensibly.

Example   The cat sprang onto the MO.   <u>USE</u>

36   The PFUL puppy followed the children around the garden.   _____

37   They invited the NEIGHBS round for a drink.   _____

38   He used CCHES for three weeks after breaking his toe.   _____

39   The FISMEN headed back to port to avoid the storm.   _____

40   The girl cried because her hamster had ESED.   _____

Move one letter from the first word and add it to the second word to make two new words.

B 13

Example   hunt   sip   *hut*   *snip*

41 sting   sea   ———   ———

42 paint   met   ———   ———

43 globe   race   ———   ———

44 pretty   each   ———   ———

45 clover   lava   ———   ———

5

Change the first word of the third pair in the same way as the other pairs to give a new word.

B 18

Example   bind, hind   bare, hare   but, *hut*

46 ever, eve   peace, pea   barren, — ———

47 near, are   phase, sea   scar, — ———

48 hat, hit   sat, sit   pat, ———

49 sent, nets   rite, tier   hems, ———

50 jet, jest   bet, best   wet, ———

5

Complete the following sentences by selecting the most sensible word from each group of words given in the brackets. Underline the words selected.

B 14

Example   The (children, books, foxes) carried the (houses, books, steps) home from the (greengrocer, library, factory).

51 The (kind, greedy, clever) (boy, dog, girl) wouldn't share his (sweets, socks, sister).

52 The cat (licked, scratched, kicked) the (oil, coffee, milk) from the (kettle, saucer, bed).

53 You can (draw, write, research) your (homework, sports, letter) on the (park, internet, envelope).

54 Mum (drove, swam, rush) to the (food, kitchen, garden) centre to buy new (plants, cars, books).

55 Please don't (watch, listen, play) (puzzles, football, drawing) near the (flowers, clouds, music).

5

A group of boys took an exam. Michael and Fahad received different marks, but their marks were both formed from the numbers 3 and 4. Michael had the lowest mark. Chen had 2 more than Michael, but 3 less than Abbas. Nicholas had eight more marks than Michael but 5 fewer than Misha.

B 25

Write the marks each boy got.

56 Michael   —   **57** Fahad   —   **58** Misha   —

59 Chen   —   **60** Abbas   —   **61** Nicholas   —

6

Fill in the crosswords so that all the given words are included. You have been given one letter as a clue in each crossword.

62–63

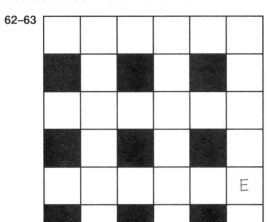

aspect, taster, endure, accrue, talent, spades

64–65

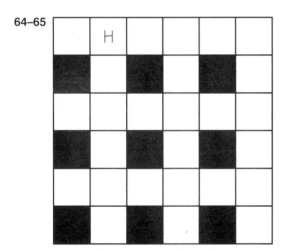

yields, hooray, offend, theory, warned, toffee

4

If a = 2, b = 3, c = 4, d = 5, e = 6, find the answer to these calculations.

66 eb = _____

67 $\dfrac{bc}{a}$ = _____

68 $\dfrac{4c}{a}$ = _____

69 2ad = _____

70 5d − 2a = _____

71 $\dfrac{2bc}{c}$ = _____

6

If the code for ILLUSTRATE is qrrstuvwux, what are the codes for the following words?

72 TREAT _____

73 SLATE _____

74 LEAST _____

What do these codes stand for?

75 vstu _____

76 rwuxv _____

5

4

Give the two missing pairs of letters in the following sequences. The alphabet has been written out to help you.

A B C D E F G H I J K L M N O P Q R S T U V W X Y Z

	Example	CQ	DQ	EP	FP	*GO*	*HO*

77 ZD   XE   VF   ___   RH   ___

78 ED   ___   II   KL   MN   ___

79 AB   ZD   BG   ___   CP   ___

80 PL   QK   ___   SI   TH   ___

If the code for PINEAPPLE is $+ - \times \% £ + + @ \%$, what are the codes for the following words?

81 LEAP _____

82 PLAIN _____

83 LINE _____

What do these codes stand for?

84 $+ £ @ \%$ _____

85 $@ £ \times \%$ _____

86 $\times £ - @$ _____

Fill in the missing letters. The alphabet has been written out to help you.

A B C D E F G H I J K L M N O P Q R S T U V W X Y Z

Example   AB is to CD as PQ is to *RS*

87 JT is to LV as SU is to _____

88 XPE is to ZNG as MVG is to _____

89 ELT is to IPX as JAR is to _____

90 JDI is to HGG as PFW is to _____

91 AXD is to ZCW as BVQ is to _____

Read the first two statements and then underline one of the four options below that must be true.

92 'Ameena flew to Italy on an aeroplane. Ameena likes to fly.'

      Ameena went on holiday to Italy.

      Flying is the quickest way to travel.

      Some aeroplanes take passengers to Italy.

      Some people are nervous of flying.

Read the first statement and then underline one of the five options below that must be true.

93 'Children going on the trip were told to take a waterproof coat with them.'

Bad weather was forecast.

It usually rains in the autumn.

The children had to spend most of the day walking around.

Children were advised to take a particular item of clothing.

Comfortable shoes should also be worn.

Read the first statement and then underline one of the five options below that must be true.

94 'Some cats and dogs need to be groomed.'

Owners should always groom their pets.

Certain animals need to be groomed.

A brush is softer than a comb.

Dog hair makes a mess in the house.

Brushes and combs for animals can be bought in pet shops.

Read the first two statements and then underline one of the five options below that must be true.

95 'The bus arrives at school at 8:45 a.m. It usually leaves school about 3:30 p.m.'

Lessons start at 9:00 a.m.

The bus belongs to the school.

Most pupils use the school bus.

The bus doesn't always leave at 3:30 p.m.

Children who miss the bus must get their parents to collect them.

4

Find a word that can be put in front of each of the following words to make new, compound words.

B | **11**

Example	CAST	FALL	WARD	POUR	<u>DOWN</u>
96 WORD	BOW	OVER	BONES		_____
97 SHOW	BOARD	KICK	TRACK		_____
98 SIDE	SHOOT	STAGE	HAND		_____
99 LAW	SIDE	RAGE	WARD		_____
100 WATER	STAND	FOOT	LINE		_____

5

Paper 2

97/100

B 5

Underline the word in the brackets closest in meaning to the word in capitals.

Example   UNHAPPY   (unkind death laughter <u>sad</u> friendly)

1 STILL   (busy soft loud quiet alone)

2 LONG   (thin brief high angry desire)

3 CALM   (wild peaceful excited stormy rough)

4 DISAPPEAR   (arrive come surface vanish emerge)

5 BRIEF   (lengthy hide wordy rambling curt)

5

Underline the one word in the brackets which will go equally well with both the pairs of words outside the brackets.

B 5

Example   rush, attack   cost, fee   (price, hasten, strike, <u>charge</u>, money)

6 receive, take   agree to, allow   (gain, obtain, believe, accept. approve)

7 dwelling, home   lecture, talk to   (house, address, location, speech, settle)

8 depart, migrate   touch, affect   (advance, impress, move, proceed, motivate)

9 condemn, attack   plague, burden   (disaster, ordeal, spell, curse, swear)

10 bathe, swim   decline, descend   (drop, dip, drench, damp, deck)

5

Find the three-letter word which can be added to the letters in capitals to make a new word. The new word will complete the sentence sensibly.

B 22

Example   The cat sprang onto the MO.   <u>USE</u>

11 Please DESCE everything you saw.   _____

12 Do you know if the house is VAT?   _____

13 The PE of lions slept in the shade.   _____

14 Adopt a more POIVE attitude to your work.   _____

15 She ran to her parents' room after hearing a STGE noise downstairs.   _____

5

Find the letter which will end the first word and start the second word.

B 10

Example   peac (<u>h</u>) ome

16 bur   (__) olk

17 sag   (__) lso

18 pin   (__) ven

19 cas   (__) not

20 fel   (__) aint

5

Change the first word into the last word, by changing one letter at a time and making a new, different word in the middle.

Example   CASE   _CASH_   LASH

21   MOST   _____   DUST

22   COST   _____   COAX

23   SAME   _____   HOME

24   LAMB   _____   GAME

25   FOUR   _____   POUT

5

Rearrange the muddled letters in capitals to make a proper word. The answer will complete the sentence sensibly.

Example   A BEZAR is an animal with stripes.   _ZEBRA_

26   A pet rabbit lives in a TUHHC.   _____

27   Low ground between two hills is called a LYALVE.   _____

28   An PTOOIN is a choice.   _____

29   RTIHBG is the opposite of dull.   _____

30   Pasta is popular in LTYAI.   _____

5

Underline the two words, one from each group, that go together to form a new word. The word in the first group always comes first.

Example   (hand, <u>green</u>, for)   (light, <u>house</u>, sure)

31   (with, wit, wish)   (on, in, it)

32   (door, house, key)   (fence, wood, board)

33   (more, last, price)   (cost, less, fix)

34   (life, watch, time)   (notice, guard, pass)

35   (arm, blaze. fight)   (are, our, hour)

5

Complete the following sentences by selecting the most sensible word from each group of words given in the brackets. Underline the words selected.

Example   The (<u>children</u>, books, foxes) carried the (houses, <u>books</u>, steps) home from the (greengrocer, <u>library</u>, factory).

36   The (girl, bird, fish) put her (food, babies, gloves) on because it was (sunny, cold. sad).

37   A (swan, fox, spider) is a (sporty, wild, slippery) (reptile, person, mammal).

38   (Funny, older, modern) (pupils, patients, drivers) should start to think about their next (parents, schools, children).

39 The (text, letter, email) was sent to their (advanced, new, ringing) (station, bedroom, house).

40 You can (take, put, steal) the money from my (folder, book, purse) for your (crime, bus fare, police).

Find and underline the two words which need to change places for each sentence to make sense.

Example   She went to <u>letter</u> the <u>write</u>.

41 Please try do to your corrections.

42 Remove it with the oven from care.

43 Dog the came in from the garden when it started to rain.

44 Let's tidy up because she will in here be a few minutes.

45 Will new clubs some be starting next term.

Change the first word of the third pair in the same way as the other pairs to give a new word.

Example   bind, hind   bare, hare   but, <u>hut</u>

46 tarnish, tar   warden, war   beetle, _____

47 mountain, tan   project, jet   entire, _____

48 hostage, tag   suspend, pen   deride, _____

49 skip, sip   sway, say   buoy, _____

50 affair, air   excel, eel   avert, _____

Fill in the crosswords so that all the given words are included. You have been given one letter as a clue in each crossword.

51–52

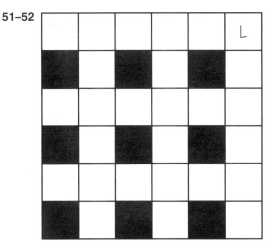

bridle, tonsil, owners, speedy, angers, losses

tokens, hungry, keener, reckon,
sketch, keeper

Fill in the missing letters. The alphabet has been written out to help you.

A B C D E F G H I J K L M N O P Q R S T U V W X Y Z

Example   AB is to CD as PQ is to R̲S̲

55 GOH is to IQJ as KSN is to _____

56 EJT is to GMX as BKP is to _____

57 CAH is to DZJ as MYP is to _____

58 BHV is to AGU as XKD is to _____

59 JZH is to LXJ as TCN is to _____

If the code for PECULIAR is 23456789, what are the codes for the following words?

60 RAIL   _____   61 PEAR   _____   62 PRICE   _____

What do these codes stand for?

63 4682   _____   64 9563   _____   65 2763   _____

Give the two missing pairs of letters in the following sequences. The alphabet has been written out to help you.

A B C D E F G H I J K L M N O P Q R S T U V W X Y Z

Example	CQ	DQ	EP	FP	G̲O̲	H̲O̲
66 KD	MG	OJ	___	___	US
67 PL	SI	VF	___	___	EW
68 NGQ	___	PES	QDT	RCU	___
69 ___	PUL	NSJ	LQH	___	HMD
70 ABC	EFG	___	MNO	QRS	___

I was three years old when my brother was born, and my sister was two years younger than me. Next year I will be twelve.

B 25

71 How old was I last year? _____

72 How old will my sister be next year? _____

73 How old will my brother be when my sister is twenty? _____

74 When my brother was six, how old was my sister? _____

4

Here are the number codes for five words. Match the right word to the right code.

B 24

4322   5123   4153   7653   5647

CURE   CELL   RULE   RICH   HIRE

75 CURE _____ **76** CELL _____ **77** RULE _____ **78** RICH _____ **79** HIRE _ _

5

If A = 1, B = 2, C = 3, D = 4 and E = 5, give the answer to the following calculations.

B 26

80 $(D \div B) + E =$ _____

81 $2C =$ _____

82 $D^2 + B^2 =$ _____

83 $E + C - B -$ _____

84 $(B^2 + C^2) - (D^2 - C^2) =$ _____

85 $(C^2 \times B^2) + (E^2 - A^2) =$ _____

6

Find a word that is similar in meaning to the word in capital letters and that rhymes with the second word.

B 5

Example   CABLE   tyre   *wire*

86 PURCHASE   shy   _____

87 SEAT   stair   _____

88 TALENT   hair   _____

89 POST   frail   _____

90 STICK   flew   _____

5

Complete the following expressions by underlining the missing word.

B 15

Example   Frog is to tadpole as swan is to (duckling, baby, <u>cygnet</u>).

91 Sharp is to blunt as major is to (main, minor, superior).

92 Revise is to correct as cure is to (remedy, illness, disease).

93 Echo is to repeat as flaw is to (perfect, loud, fault).

94 Spare is to extra as sincere is to (false, deceitful, genuine).

95 Protect is to harm as abandon is to (desert, claim, keep).

5

Which word in each group contains only the first six letters of the alphabet? Underline the answer.

B 18

Example	defeat	farce	abide	<u>deaf</u>	dice
96	able	fade	cage	badge	each
97	dale	aback	deal	deed	beak
98	cake	bale	babe	cable	feel
99	behalf	acid	ache	cash	beef
100	dead	adage	action	cadge	frame

5

Now go to the Progress Chart to record your score!   Total   100

Paper 3

Look at these groups of words.

B 1

A	B	C	D
caterpillar	palace	herd	cousin
tadpole	house	pride	nephew
calf	bungalow	flock	sister

Choose the correct group for each of the words below. Write in the letter.

1–5 fawn __   chalet __   uncle __   castle __

igloo __   swarm __   parents __   cub __

gosling __   litter __

5

Find two letters which will end the first word and start the second word.

B 10

Example   rea (<u>c h</u>) air

6 plur (__ __) so

7 trav (__ __) egant

8 drea (__ __) stery

9 flow (__ __) ase

10 pala (__ __) nsor

5

Find the three-letter word which can be added to the letters in capitals to make a new word. The new word will complete the sentence sensibly.

Example   The cat sprang onto the MO.   USE

11 The weather was FLY good all day.   _____

12 My BHER cannot come out until he has tidied his room.   _____

13 Some children get BD during long school holidays.   _____

14 She wrote PRIE on the cover of her diary.   _____

15 I EFULLY noted down the telephone number.   _____   ⬤ 5

Underline the one word in the brackets which will go equally well with both the pairs of words outside the brackets.

Example   rush, attack   cost, fee   (price, hasten, strike, <u>charge</u>, money)

16 protect, shelter   lid, roof   (top, blanket, safe, cover, box)

17 unfriendly, hostile   foreign, different   (enemy, alien, abroad, separate, unusual)

18 finish, end   whole, undivided   (achieved, all, total, close, complete)

19 goodwill, kindness   approval, prefer   (like, favour, service, back, spoil)

20 outburst, row   place, site   (circumstances, location, outlook, scene, tantrum)   ⬤ 5

Underline the two words, one from each group, which are closest in meaning.

Example   (race, shop, <u>start</u>)   (finish, <u>begin</u>, end)

21 (control, convenience, effort)   (discomfort, confusion, ease)

22 (temper, bright, reassure)   (depress, encourage, endear)

23 (futile, affect, banish)   (profitable, admit, fruitless)

24 (mind, merge, club)   (mix, divide, social)

25 (commute, place, inhabit)   (household, occupy, resident)   ⬤ 5

Find the four-letter word hidden at the end of one word and the beginning of the next word. The order of the letters may not be changed.

Example   The children had bats and balls.   *sand*

26 Don't drop lotion on the towel.   _____

27 That match appeared live on television.   _____

28 We often hear children playing in the street.   _____

29 I made all the cakes for Connor's birthday party.   _____

30 I am aiming to finish this by Friday.   _____   ⬤ 5

Find and underline the two words which need to change places for each sentence to make sense.

B 17

Example   She went to <u>letter</u> the <u>write</u>.

31 I can't concentrate on the television is when.

32 In month the weather has been sunnier than this August.

33 I must water the plants while vou am out.

34 She is saving a money to buy her new hamster cage.

35 Don't hear off until you set the whistle blow.

5

Underline the two words which are the odd ones out in the following groups of words.

B 5

Example	black	king	purple	green	house
36 duck	waddles	eagle	nest		heron
37 local	alien	foreigner	native		stranger
38 post	letter	column	newspaper		stake
39 idle	busy	lazy	foolish		unproductive
40 windy	snowing	pretty	horrible		raining

5

Read the first two statements and then underline one of the five options below that must be true.

B 25

41 'Elena's father is Italian. Her father's parents still live in Italy.'

Elena can speak Italian.

Elena goes to Italy at least once a year.

Elena's father no longer lives in Italy.

Elena has grandparents who live in Italy.

Rome is the capital of Italy.

Read the first two statements and then underline one of the five options below that must be true.

42 'My sister is expecting a baby. The baby might be a girl.'

My sister would rather have a girl.

My sister has bought pink baby clothes.

The doctor thinks it's a girl.

Doctors work in hospitals.

My sister might have a boy.

Read the first two statements and then underline one of the five options below that must be true.

43 'Many people have cars. Some buy expensive cars.'

People prefer cheaper cars.

Some people have expensive cars.

Old cars usually cost less.

Sports cars are always expensive.

Expensive cars use a lot of petrol.

Read the first two statements and then underline one of the five options below that must be true.

44 'Year 6 pupils went on a trip to France. Most mornings they went to the bakery.'

France is famous for nice bread.

The children bought bread at the bakery.

The children spoke French in the bakery.

Bread is eaten with jam for breakfast.

Sometimes the children went to the bakery.

Look at the first group of three words. The word in the middle has been made from the other two words. Complete the second group of three words in the same way, making a new word in the middle.

Example	PAIN	INTO	TOOK	ALSO	*SOON*	ONLY
45 LEFT	TALE	SACK	KEEL	————		FILM
46 LONG	GOAL	FAIL	CALF	————		ACNE
47 GRIP	PAGE	DEAF	SAID	————		STUN
48 BYTE	BEAT	CAKE	EACH	————		WISP
49 URGE	BEAR	BAIL	IDEA	————		CROP
50 BOARD	SOLD	CLOSE	LEASE	————		PRIDE

Complete the following sentences by selecting the most sensible word from each group of words given in the brackets. Underline the words selected.

Example   The (children, books, foxes) carried the (houses, books, steps) home from the (greengrocer, library, factory).

51 I (hurt, looked, cheated) my (book, finger, window) playing (homework, texting, netball).

52 Please (make, buy, sell) some (ham, cake, sweets) and I'll make us a (mess, drink, sandwich) for lunch.

53 Our (grandmother, baby, tree) will be (years, thousands, seventy) next (minute, day, week).

54 Over the (last, present, next) few years I have (went, come, been) to the cinema (frequently, slowly, unusually).

55 If you (scribble, take, send) lots of (sketches, stories, texts), your parents will (reward, complain, smile) about the bill.

5

Fill in the crosswords so that all the given words are included. You have been given one letter as a clue in each crossword.

B 19

56–57

recede, deceit, annexe, client,
fennel, severe

58–59

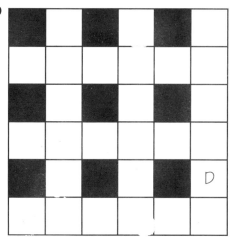

temple, stress, staple, breeds,
rarest, barter

4

Give the missing numbers in the following sequences.

Example	2	4	6	8	<u>10</u>	<u>12</u>

60	40	80	35	88	—	—
61	3	3	6	18	—	360
62	14	16	19	—	28	—
63	—	23	16	10	—	1
64	—	58	45	34	25	—

5

On the street below live five families. The Li family live in a house with an even number. The Wilmots are on the same side of the street as the Journeauxs but are not next door to them. The Singhs live across the street from the Hicks and next door to the Wilmots. The Journeauxs house looks onto the park.

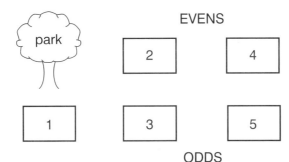

Write the name of the family that lives in each of the following houses.

65 1 _____ **66** 2 _____ **67** 3 _____

68 4 _____ **69** 5 _____

5

If the code for INCUBATE is @ £ $ + % − × 0, what are the codes for the following words?

70 BITE _____ **71** ACT _____ **72** CABIN _____

What do these codes stand for?

73 × + % 0 _____ **74** % 0 − × _____ **75** × + £ 0 _____

6

Which one letter can be added to the front of all the words to make new words?

B 12

Example   <u>c</u>are   <u>c</u>at   <u>c</u>rate   <u>c</u>all

76 ___ell   ___hap   ___harm   ___heat   ___heck

77 ___ilt   ___ill   ___ike   ___oarse   ___uddle

78 ___ose   ___uff   ___rove   ___roud   ___ick

79 ___haw   ___est   ___ale   ___aper   ___aut

80 ___ell   ___arn   ___ard   ___ield   ___outh

5

If A = 2, B = 4, C = 5, D = 6, E = 8 and F = 9, find the sum of the following words by adding the letters together.

B 26

81 BEAD   _____   82 FADE   _____

83 FEED   _____   84 CEDE   _____

85 DEAF   _____

5

Underline the two words, one from each group, which are the most opposite in meaning.

B 9

Example   (dawn, <u>early</u>, wake)   (<u>late</u>, stop, sunrise)

86 (exaggerate, exact, expand)   (definite, enlarge, imprecise)

87 (security, isolate, insult)   (offend, praise, upset)

88 (ever, extra, moor)   (more, always, never)

89 (rarity, common, ready)   (shortage, frequency, eager)

90 (flashing, shouting, hazardous)   (uncertain, safe, warning)

5

Remove one letter from the word in capital letters to leave a new word. The meaning of the new word is given in the clue.

B 12

Example   AUNT   an insect   <u>ant</u>

91 CLASH   money   _____

92 STORMY   legend   _____

93 BARGE   exposed   _____

94 WAIVE   use hand in greeting   _____

95 KNIT   equipment   _____

5

Underline the two words which are made from the same letters.

Example	TAP	PET	<u>TEA</u>	POT	<u>EAT</u>
96 PACK	CARE	CARP	RACK	RACE
97 FIST	SOFT	HOST	THAT	SHOT
98 STEEL	STALL	LEAST	STALE	TEASE
99 ONCE	NONE	CONES	NEON	SCORE
100 ANTLER	ANTHEM	TALENT	LEARNT	THEME

5

Now go to the Progress Chart to record your score! Total 100

Paper 4

94/00

Underline one word in the brackets which is most opposite in meaning to the word in capitals.

Example WIDE (broad vague long <u>narrow</u> motorway)

1 FOOLISH (wise crazy absurd simple weak)

2 BOOK (album note register cancel reserve)

3 SOCIABLE (hostile outgoing approachable organised serious)

4 FIERCE (cruel aggressive gentle intense grim)

5 PERFECT (excellent flawed exact ideal entire)

5

Underline the one word in the brackets which will go equally well with both the pairs of words outside the brackets.

Example rush, attack cost, fee (price, hasten, strike, <u>charge</u>, money)

6 answer, explanation liquid, mixture (key, response, blend, solution, settle)

7 register, file achievement, personal best (account. record, report, track, performance)

8 issue, concern important, count (subject. event. matter, stuff, worry)

9 rub, scrape bars, fireplace (burn, fuel, grind, grate, scratch)

10 quick, brisk cross, irritable (hasty, lively, sluggish, snappy, snarling)

5

19

Find the three-letter word which can be added to the letters in capitals to make a new word. The new word will complete the sentence sensibly.

B 22

> **Example**   The cat sprang onto the MO.   <u>USE</u>

11 She took her prescription straight to the CIST.   _____

12 INGIENTS are usually listed at the start of a recipe.   _____

13 We RLY watch our old videos.   _____

14 Luckily most local INHAANTS were moved to safety before the volcano erupted.   _____

15 Adequate PREPAION is essential before any exam.   _____

5

Find two letters which will end the first word and start the second word.

B 10

> **Example**   rea (<u>c h</u>) air

16 cra (__ __) ade

17 sha (__ __) sh

18 spa (__ __) corate

19 tr   (__ __) rie

20 ma (__ __) side

5

Underline the one word in the brackets closest in meaning to the word in capitals.

B 5

> **Example**   UNHAPPY   (unkind death laughter <u>sad</u> friendly)

21 ANSWER   (responsible question argue respond tick)

22 COMMON   (grass garden weed unusual ordinary)

23 PROBLEM   (sum hard solution difficulty impossible)

24 FIND   (lose reward discover decision evidence)

25 PART   (divide fracture whole chorus play)

5

Find a word that can be put in front of each of the following words to make new, compound words.

B 11

> **Example**   CAST   FALL   WARD   POUR   <u>DOWN</u>

26 COURT   CAST   GO   GROUND   _____

27 LIKE   BIRTH   HOOD   MINDER   _____

28 BOARD   BAND   LIGHT   STONE   _____

29 LANCE   WAY   WHEEL   STYLE   _____

30 LETTER   FLASH   PAPER   AGENT   _____

5

Complete the following sentences by selecting the most sensible word from each group of words given in the brackets. Underline the words selected.

B 14

Example The (<u>children</u>, books, foxes) carried the (houses, <u>books</u>, steps) home from the (greengrocer, <u>library</u>, factory).

31 The (child, children, pupil) argue about (which, what, who) can use the (timetable, outing, computer).

32 We can go (by, past, through) train to the (stick, match, burn) next (tomorrow, yesterday, week).

33 My dog is losing the (sound, taste, sight) in her (right, correct, wrong) (leg, tail, eye).

34 Can I go to (village, country, town) with my (pets, friends, enemies) after (school, dentist, shop)?

35 Don't (play, use, mention) the (email, calculator, radio) to do these (sums, pictures, art).

5

Complete the following expressions by underlining the missing word.

B 15

Example Frog is to tadpole as swan is to (duckling, baby, <u>cygnet</u>).

36 Sensible is to reasonable as childish is to (family, trusting, immature, perfect, weak).

37 Bad is to evil as good is to (fresh, wicked, skilled, worthy, corrupt).

38 Glare is to scowl as spot is to (clean, clothes, skin, eye, see).

39 Temporary is to permanent as eternal is to (changeable, heaven, airy, endless, undying).

40 Rapid is to fast as slow is to (hectic, rushed, quiet, hurried, leisurely).

5

Rearrange the muddled letters in capitals to make a proper word. The answer will complete the sentence sensibly.

B 16

Example A BEZAR is an animal with stripes.   ZEBRA

41 A CHEAP is a type of summer fruit.   _____

42 A MASTER is a small river.   _____

43 TRAINS is to stretch or draw tight.   _____

44 A VIRAL is someone against whom one competes.   _____

45 STOAT is to brown something, such as a piece of bread.   _____

5

Underline two words, one from each group, that go together to form a new word. The word in the first group always comes first.

B 8

Example (hand, <u>green</u>, for)   (light, <u>house</u>, sure)

46 (all, never, ever)   (body, less, green)

47 (tail, meet, slow)   (wag, or, up)

48 (all, whole, half)   (low, day, way)

49 (ship, pay, bread)   (role, slip, meant)

50 (not, note, cub)   (now, able, board)

5

knuckle   kinetic   kindle   kidney   kettle

51 Which word contains the letter nearest to the end of the alphabet? _____

52 Which word has the most vowels in it? _____

53 Which vowel is used in all the words? _____

54 Which letter occurs once in KIDNEY and KINDLE and twice in KINETIC? _____

55 Write the words in alphabetical order.

_____   _____   _____   _____   _____

Fill in the crosswords so that all the given words are included. You have been given one letter as a clue in each crossword.

56–57

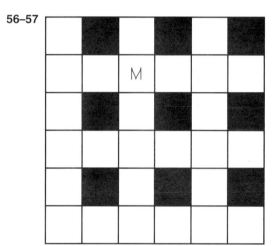

sleepy, dispel, number, people,
embers, unused

58–59

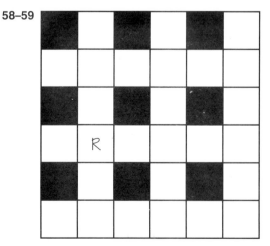

bikini, adhere, rewind, aspire,
braise, learns

Give the missing numbers in the following sequences.

	Example	2	4	6	8	<u>10</u>	<u>12</u>
60	15	15	16	18	—	—
61	33	36	40	43	—	—
62	48	9	24	—	—	36
63	—	64	—	36	25	16
64	8	16	—	24	24	—

5

If the code for FRAGMENT is PSUWCXZG, what are the codes for the following words?

65 GEAR _____   **66** FRAME _____   **67** GATE _____

What do these codes stand for?

68 PXUS _____   **69** GUCX _____   **70** SUPG _____

6

If A = 4, B = 6, C = 5, D = 8 and E = 3, give the answers to these calculations as letters.

71 $A \times B = D \times$?   __

72 $A^2 = E + C +$?   __

73 $(D \times E) + B = ? \times C$ __

74 $A + B + E = ? + D$ __

75 $B^2 - A^2 = C \times$?   __

5

Change the first word of the third pair in the same way as the other pairs to give a new word.

	Example	bind, hind	bare, hare	but, <u>hut</u>
76	kink, ink	late, ate	pour, _____
77	lamb, lame	comb, come	hard, _____
78	debit, bite	medal, dale	petal, _____
79	frail, grail	crown, drown	soil, _____
80	alter, tear	ember, beer	expel, _____

5

Here are the number codes for six words. Match the right word to the right code.

1634	3527	2534	3641	2633	4653
FALL	FILM	LAMP	LIFT	MAIL	PALM

81 FALL _____   **82** FILM _____   **83** LAMP _____

84 LIFT _____   **85** MAIL _____   **86** PALM _____

6

Read the first two statements and then underline one of the five options below that must be true.

87 'Fractions are sums. Some children find fractions hard.'

       Fractions are always hard.

       Most children like maths.

       Children should be able to do fractions.

       Children find certain sums hard.

       It's easier to use a calculator for difficult sums.

Read the first two statements and then underline one of the five options below that must be true.

88 'Jamille plans to catch the bus into town at 11:30 a.m. The bus can be up to 10 minutes late.'

       Jamille knows he will have to wait for the bus.

       Public transport is often reliable.

       Jamille will be late to meet his friends.

       The bus will have arrived by 11:40 a.m.

       Jamille prefers his mum to take him in the car.

Read the first two statements and then underline one of the five options below that must be true.

89 'Sarah is 17 years old. You can learn to drive at 17.'

       Sarah has started driving lessons.

       Most people start learning to drive at 17.

       It is best to have lessons from a qualified instructor.

       Sarah's parents have bought her a car.

       Sarah can now learn to drive.

Read the first two statements and then underline one of the five options below that must be true.

90 'Sprouts are green. Sprouts are vegetables.'

       Carrots are not green.

       Not all vegetables are green.

       Sprouts are green vegetables.

       Sprouts are sold in supermarkets.

       Green vegetables are good for you.

4

A, B, C, D and E have mobile phones.

A and E have pink phones, the others have silver ones.

B, D and E can access the internet on their phones, the others cannot.

A, B and E just send text messages, the others text and make calls.

B 25

91 Who has a silver phone used just for texting?   _____

92 Who has internet access on a pink phone?   _____

93 Who has a silver phone, but no internet access?   _____

94 Who has internet access and makes calls?   _____

4

Fill in the missing letters. The alphabet has been written out to help you.

B 23

A B C D E F G H I J K L M N O P Q R S T U V W X Y Z

Example   AB is to CD as PQ is to RS

95 GI is to JF as NK is to   _____

96 BU is to CV as HM is to   _ _

97 QJ is to SM as FO is to   _____

98 WX is to DC as ZY is to   _____

99 UG is to TF as ME is to   _____

100 BW is to AX as ZZ is to   _____

6

Now go to the Progress Chart to record your score!   Total   **100**

Paper 5

Underline the two words, one from each group, which are closest in meaning.

B 3

Example   (race, shop, start)   (finish, begin, end)

1 (defer, defend, define)   (shift, shield, attack)

2 (distress, remote, remove)   (comfort, alert, distant)

3 (hint, advice, gossip)   (helper, notify, trace)

4 (paper, administration, stationary)   (pens, computer, immobile)

5 (fine, lovely, nice)   (clever, thick, thin)

5

Underline the pair of words most opposite in meaning.

Example   cup, mug   coffee, milk   <u>hot, cold</u>

6 company, firm   compete, contend   dislike, prefer

7 ideal, best   splendid, drab   disarray, chaos

8 picture, imagine   intention, goal   interest, boredom

9 provide, remove   publish, print   health, diet

10 regal, noble   primitive, developed   priceless, costly

Find the three-letter word which can be added to the letters in capitals to make a new word. The new word will complete the sentence sensibly.

Example   The cat sprang onto the MO.   <u>USE</u>

11 What time does the train DEP?   _____

12 The foal trotted along beside its MOT.   _____

13 It takes a lot of COUE to sing on your own in a concert.   _____

14 I'm amazed that you managed to do the LE test.   _____

15 If you play football at lunchtime, your school TRORS will get dirty. _____

Change the first word into the last word by changing one letter at a time and making a new, different word in the middle.

Example   CASE   <u>CASH</u>   LASH

16 WIND   _____   SINK

17 DOZE   _____   MAZE

18 SAIL   _____   SAND

19 DOTE   _____   LOVE

20 TOLD   _____   ROAD

Complete the following sentences by selecting the most sensible word from each group of words given in the brackets. Underline the words selected.

Example   The (<u>children</u>, books, foxes) carried the (houses, <u>books</u>, steps) home from the (greengrocer, <u>library</u>, factory).

21 She (watched, scored, marked) the correct (answer, idea, effort) with a (cross, dot, tick).

22 The puppy was (licked, fed, trained) to (bite, sit, scratch) (lively, quietly, noisily).

23 He (left, bought, gave) his (cat, sweater, soap) in the (library, fridge, oven).

24 (Grass, Smoke, Plastic) melts (in, out, off) extreme (cold, ice, heat).

25 We need to (fetch, get, look) you a new (glove, boot, coat) for the (spell, winter, weathered).

Find the four-letter word hidden at the end of one word and the beginning of the next word. The order of the letters may not be changed.

Example   The children had bats and balls.   _sand_

26 He chose to have a swimming party.   _____

27 The head teacher is dealing with an issue affecting every class.   _____

28 He climbed over the fence and jumped down onto the grass.   _____

29 After school we sometimes ride about the park on our bikes.   _____

30 Staff offer individual pupils help if needed.   _____   **5**

Look at the first group of three words. The word in the middle has been made from the other two words. Complete the second group of three words in the same way, making a new word in the middle.

	Example	PAIN	INTO	TOOK	ALSO	_SOON_	ONLY
31	HIDE	MAID	NAME		ITEM	_____	FIST
32	SORRY	ROSE	SENSE		MOANS	_____	NAÏVE
33	TREK	LATE	NAIL		FATE	_____	LAIR
34	RAIL	RATE	TEAR		PAIN	_____	AREA
35	REAL	HARE	HEEL		WEAN	_____	FOND
36	PIPE	COPE	CODE		RULE	_____	RAIN

6

Find the letter which will complete both pairs of words, ending the first word and starting the second. The same letter must be used for both pairs of words.

Example   mea (t) able   fi (t) ub

37 dee (__) efy   woo (__) eck

38 plat (__) vent   crat (__) nvy

39 chil (__) ead   coi (__) atch

40 shar (__) ost   was (__) ump

41 boa (__) ole   moo (__) eal   **5**

Move one letter from the first word and add it to the second word to make two new words.

Example   hunt   sip   _hut_   _snip_

42 caper   eel   _____   _____

43 niche   sift   _____   _____

44 tang   tee   _____   _____

45 raft   rail   _____   _____

46 sidle   pay   _____   _____   **5**

Complete the following expressions by underlining the missing word.

B 15

Example   Frog is to tadpole as swan is to (duckling, baby, <u>cygnet</u>).

47 Cow is to beef as pig is to (sty, piglet, pork, grunt, farm).

48 Sleep is to slept as go is to (come, going, travel, went, goodbye).

49 Boat is to water as car is to (garage, road, driver, petrol, fast).

50 Eager is to keen as essential is to (needless, indispensable, nonsense, useless, normal).

51 Pleasure is to pain as crooked is to (bent, curved, crafty, shady, straight).

5

Underline the word in the brackets which goes best with the words given outside the brackets.

B 1

Example   word, paragraph, sentence   (pen, cap, <u>letter</u>, top, stop)

52 oak, fir   (bluebell, primrose, palm, parsley, bean)

53 serious, grave   (absurd, helpless, solemn, lazy, foolish)

54 quarrel, disagree   (settle, satisfy, permit, allow, dispute)

55 midnight, dawn   (atmosphere, cloudy, horizon, sunset, planet)

56 greet, salute   (ignore, welcome, frighten, march, pleased)

5

Underline the two words which are the odd ones out in the following groups of words.

B 4

Example   black   <u>king</u>   purple   green   <u>house</u>

57 cheap   expensive   dear   loved   costly

58 breed   type   raise   lower   nurture

59 total   number   question increase   add

60 wind   blow   thump   damage   punch

61 author   poem   sketch   poet   artist

5

Find and underline the two words which need to change places for each sentence to make sense.

B 17

Example   She went to <u>letter</u> the <u>write</u>.

62 Polish must you your shoes before tomorrow.

63 The sun came just out after lunch.

64 It is now too complicated to explain far.

65 Add the teabag and remove some milk.

66 She made one new friends after just two day.

5

Underline two words, one from each group, that go together to form a new word. The word in the first group always comes first.

Example   (hand, <u>green</u>, for)   (light, <u>house</u>, sure)

67 (rest, wonder, ward)   (full, ore, den)

68 (car, sand, on)   (our, pit, nest)

69 (split, miss, bar)   (gin, row, take)

70 (writ, bite, grow)   (err, up, ten)

71 (up, prop, red)   (shore, dish, pose)

5

Which one letter can be added to the front of all these words to make new words?

Example   _c_are   _c_at   _c_rate   _c_all

72 ___each   ___eact   ___ead   ___ear   ___eign

73 ___ack   ___alt   ___eed   ___uit   ___igh

74 ___rim   ___art   ___uff   ___ark   ___ick

75 ___eat   ___ush   ___aul   ___ack   ___and

76 ___ury   ___ulky   ___oom   ___est   ___ank

5

Fill in the crosswords so that all the given words are included. You have been given one letter as a clue in each crossword.

77–78

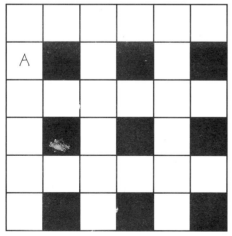

engine, ravage, morsel, rivals,
island, margin

29

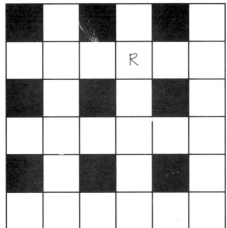

pander, sweets, trains, marrow,
wrists, advise

Give the two missing pairs of letters in the following sequences. The alphabet has been written out to help you.

A B C D E F G H I J K L M N O P Q R S T U V W X Y Z

	Example	CQ	DQ	EP	FP	<u>GO</u>	<u>HO</u>
81	PX	QW	___	SU	TT	___	
82	DH	EI	GK	JN	___	___	
83	AC	TB	BA	SZ	___	___	
84	___	SG	QI	OK	MM	___	
85	EF	HI	KL	NO	___	___	

If the code for DOCUMENT is ! × + @ ? £ O =, what are the codes for the following words?

86 CODE _____   **87** TEND _____

88 DUET _____   **89** TUNE _____

What do these codes stand for?

90 O @ = _____   **91** + × ? £ _____

92 ! @ O £ _____   **93** O × = £ _____

If S = 2, W = 3, R = 4, B = 5 and N = 6, find the answers to the following calculations.

94 $(S \times W) + N =$ _____   **95** $R + N - S =$ _____   **96** $B^2 - R^2 =$ _____

97 $2S + W^2 =$ _____   **98** $2N + 3W =$ _____   **99** $N - S + W =$ _____

100 $(B \times S) + W =$ _____

4

B 23

5

B 24

8

B 26

7

Now go to the Progress Chart to record your score!   Total   100

Paper 6

95/100

Underline the two words which are the odd ones out in the following groups of words.

B 4

Example	black	<u>king</u>	purple	green	<u>house</u>

1 bounce   spring   autumn   leap   weather

2 sponsor   form   back   run   finance

3 fork   plate   glass   spoon   knife

4 disperse   appear   show   vanish   emerge

5 area   perimeter   edge   district   region

 5

Underline the pair of words most similar in meaning.

B 5

Example   come, go   <u>roam, wander</u>   fear, fare

6 desert, abandon   fierce, fiend   pay, take

7 raw, cooked   realise, reassure   swell, bulge

8 doubtful, acceptable   means, resources   meek, arrogant

9 agree, upset   brief, long   allow, permit

10 admire, despise   underline, emphasise   calm, confused

 5

Find the three-letter word which can be added to the letters in capitals to make a new word. The new word will complete the sentence sensibly.

B 22

Example   The cat sprang onto the MO.   <u>USE</u>

11 Kate loves to play on the SES at the playground.

12 My mum's started a computer CSE to brush up her office skills.

13 She always keeps her purse in her HBAG.

14 Nina was caught in the rain and got SED.

15 TH the ball to me!

 5

Underline one word in the brackets which is most opposite in meaning to the word in capitals.

B 6

Example   WIDE   (broad   vague   long   <u>narrow</u>   motorway)

16 STRONG   (powerful   healthy   weak   athletic   determined)

17 LOST   (find   found   finding   finds   founded)

18 HEIGHTEN   (increase   improve   ceiling   prefer   diminish)

19 UNITE   (team   combine   marriage   separate   agreement)

20 CUT   (chop   hair   increase   shorten   share)

 5

Find two letters which will end the first word and start the second word.

Example   rea   (<u>c h</u>)   air

21   ext   (— —)   bbit

22   mou   (— —)   nse

23   dep   (— —)   irty

24   kenn   (— —)   astic

25   cru   (— —)   uff

26   compe   (— —)   rrible

B 10

6

Underline two words, one from each group, that go together to form a new word. The word in the first group always comes first.

Example   (hand, <u>green</u>, for)   (light, <u>house</u>, sure)

27   (peel, tall, grape)   (tree, skin, fruit)

28   (down, fast, loose)   (under, load, ten)

29   (bat, ball, show)   (wide, he, win)

30   (fur, draw, as)   (set, chart, nice)

31   (foot, neck, ear)   (pierce, pain, ring)

B 8

5

Find a word that can be put in front of each of the following words to make new, compound words.

Example   CAST   FALL   WARD   POUR   <u>DOWN</u>

32	FLY	CUP	FINGERS	MILK	————
33	BIN	MAN	PAN	CART	————
34	HEAD	STRIPE	POINT	PRICK	————
35	LAND	LOUSE	WORK	PILE	————
36	SHINE	RISE	STROKE	LIGHT	————

B 11

5

Move one letter from the first word and add it to the second word to make two new words.

Example   hunt   sip   <u>hut</u>   <u>snip</u>

37	belt	ink	————	————
38	scale	pith	————	————
39	dune	doe	————	————
40	limp	lie	————	————
41	score	mat	————	————

B 13

5

Underline the one word in the brackets which will go equally well with both the pairs of words outside the brackets.

Example rush, attack   cost, fee   (price, hasten, strike, <u>charge</u>, money)

42 ruin, damage   overprotect, pamper   (ignore, indulge, baby, spoil, destroy)

43 quite, rather   honestly, legally   (really, fully, fairly, justly, properly)

44 farmland, rural   nation, state   (kingdom, people, landscape, outdoors, country)

45 puzzle, think   marvel, miracle   (question, excellent, wonder, wonderful, speculate)

46 give, hand   succeed, qualify   (transfer, allow, past, pass, graduate)

5

Complete the following sentences by selecting the most sensible word from each group of words given in the brackets. Underline the words selected.

Example The (<u>children</u>, books, foxes) carried the (houses, <u>books</u>, steps) home from the (greengrocer, <u>library</u>, factory).

47 We can (<u>take</u>, teach, tell) your friend (house, room, home) early (tomorrow, yesterday, breakfast).

48 I've (drawn, decorated, written) the house with (shells, daisies, holly) ready for (Easter, Halloween, Christmas).

49 My (word, number, story) has to be handed (on, in, off) (next, soon, following) week.

50 I'll (pay, sell, buy) you for the (tickets, children, friends) when I (ignore, hear, see) you.

51 Coffee (tastes, sounds, touches) too (hot, dark, sweet) if you add lots of (milk, powder, sugar).

5

Complete the following expressions by filling in the missing word.

Example Pen is to ink as brush is to *paint*.

52 Interior is to inside as exterior is to _____.

53 Wrist is to cuff as neck is to _____.

54 Thermometer is to temperature as clock is to _____.

55 Petals are to flower as spokes are to _____.

56 Orange is to peel as egg is to _____.

57 Who is to person as where is to _____.

6

Underline the two words, one from each group, which are the most opposite in meaning.

Example (dawn, <u>early</u>, wake)   (<u>late</u>, stop, sunrise)

58 (official, offensive, often)   (generally, pleasant, plead)

59 (sprint, abandon, maintain)   (run, certain, neglect)

60 (endanger, guard, assure)   (enclose, protect, promise)

33

61 (deteriorate, condition, declaration)   (deviate, reiect. imnrove)

62 (speed, swift, street)   (slow, rapid. lane)

5

B 16

Rearrange the muddled letters in capitals to make a proper word. The answer will complete the sentence sensibly.

Example   A BEZAR is an animal with stripes.   ZEBRA

63 Please read the important IOCNTE below.   _____

64 I have known my best NRIFED since playgroup.   _____

65 Can I blow out the LADCNE now?   _____

66 Schools should provide healthy ELMAS for pupils.   _____

67 I don't mind RHISNAG with you.   _____

5

B 18

Look at the first group of three words. The word in the middle has been made from the other two words. Complete the second group of three words in the same way, making a new word in the middle.

Example	PAIN	INTO	TOOK	ALSO	SOON	ONLY
68 DALE	LIME	MICE		COPE	_____	LUMP
69 MUSE	TERM	DIRT		TYRE	_____	DRAB
70 GIFT	GRIT	GIRL		EASY	_____	CALL
71 TOPIC	COLT	WORLD		MUNCH	_____	MEALS
72 PLUM	MELT	TIRE		CLIP	_____	TALE
73 RAISE	SLIDE	DEALS		START	_____	CLONE

6

B 19

Fill in the crosswords so that all the given words are included. You have been given one letter as a clue in each crossword.

74–75

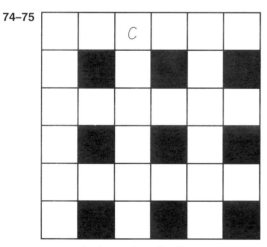

sanded, confer, docile, seesaw,
disuse, leeway

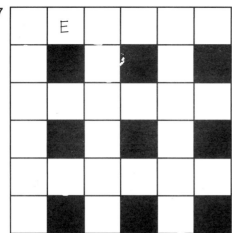

relied, tirade, nature, scroll,
nestle, lodger

A B C D E F G H I J K L M N O P Q R S T U V W X Y Z

78 If the code for NOTICE is JMRAXC, what is the code for ONCE? _____

79 If the code for ANGLE is PBVKH, what does KHPB stand for? _____

80 If the code for MILK is NHMJ, what is the code for DRINK? _____

81 If the code for DAY is WZB, what does ILLU stand for? _____

Fill in the missing letters. The alphabet has been written out to help you.

A B C D E F G H I J K L M N O P Q R S T U V W X Y Z

Example AB is to CD as PQ is to RS

82 XQ is to WP as KE is to ____

83 FH is to DJ as LW is to ____

84 BA is to WV as CU is to ____

85 IG is to KI as CN is to ____

86 FB is to UY as HD is to ____

My watch is 10 minutes slow. In 15 minutes it will say 11:20 a.m.

87 What is the correct time now? _____

88 What time did my watch say 20 minutes ago? _____

89 What will the correct time be 35 minutes from now? _____

90 What time will my watch say one hour from now? _____

Give the missing numbers in the following sequences.

| **Example** | 2 | 4 | 6 | 8 | <u>10</u> | 12 |

91	4	3	9	8	16	—	25
92	11	16	12	15	13	—	
93	56	49	43	38	—	31	
94	500	250	400	—	300	150	
95	15	17	21	23	27	—	

If the code for UNSOCIABLE is × ! $ £ = + O − ? @, what are the codes for the following words?

96 BASE _____ 97 LABEL _____ 98 SLICE _____

What do these codes stand for?

99 =?×− _____ 100 −+O$ _____

Now go to the Progress Chart to record your score! Total

Paper 7

94/100

Underline the two words, one from each group, which are closest in meaning.

Example (race, shop, <u>start</u>) (finish, <u>begin</u>, end)

1 (answer. dramatic, drastic) (ignore, reaction, normal)

2 (exact, enable. example) (valuable, toy, model)

3 (rare, rather, stale) (unusual. common, fresh)

4 (access, accident. excuse) (exit, entrance, planned)

5 (prevent, forecast. rear) (weather, predict, forefront)

Find the four-letter word hidden at the end of one word and the beginning of the next word. The order of the letters may not be changed.

Example The children had bats and balls. <u>sand</u>

6 Our dog catches fleas each time it sneaks next door. _____

7 I notice how rapidly he answers the questions. _____

8 Take the rhubarb out of the saucepan before it burns. _____

9 Tick items off the list as you place them in our trolley. _____

10 See the decorations sparkle and shimmer. _____

Underline the two words, one from each group, that go together to form a new word. The word in the first group always comes first.

Example (hand, <u>green</u>, for) (light, <u>house</u>, sure)

11 (so, add, can)   (verse, her, me)

12 (tap, con, snap)   (duct, fir, pea)

13 (past, high, out)   (word, up, come)

14 (beat, lay, dab)   (ten, bell, bed)

15 (set, sit, trust)   (tea, worthy, on)

5

Find the three-letter word which can be added to the letters in capitals to make a new word. The new word will complete the sentence sensibly.

Example The cat sprang onto the MO.   <u>USE</u>

16 The PRIER escaped some time after lunch.   _____

17 She was UNAE of the trouble she had caused.   _____

18 Tourists often choose to visit the MONUT.   _____

19 She was CUTG the fabric carefully to make a dress.   _____

20 I've ordered some clothes from the new CATAUE.   _____

5

Find the letter which will complete both pairs of words, ending the first word and starting the second. The same letter must be used for both pairs of words.

Example mea (<u>t</u>) able   fi (<u>t</u>) ub

21 dus (___) een   bac (___) ind

22 pal (___) cho   lac (___) agle

23 son (___) ate   rin (___) arage

24 coas (___) hick   bea (___) opic

25 towe (___) efer   wide (___) eal

5

Underline the one word in the brackets which will go equally well with both pairs of words or phrases outside the brackets.

Example rush, attack   cost, fee   (price, hasten, strike, <u>charge</u>, money)

26 ailment, disorder   criticism, moan   (charge, disease, grumble, groan, complaint)

27 angry, fuming   devoted, keen   (furious, sensible, mad, enthusiastic, irrational)

28 damp, soaked   weak, soppy   (soft, dry, strong, wet, humid)

37

29 refuse, reject	dwindle, flag	(decrease, decay, degenerate, decline, deteriorate)
30 fast, brisk	clever, sharp	(quick, sluggish, ready, sudden, intelligent)

Complete the following sentences by selecting the most sensible word from each group of words given in the brackets. Underline the words selected.

Example The (<u>children</u>, books, foxes) carried the (houses, <u>books</u>, steps) home from the (greengrocer, <u>library</u>, factory).

31 We (waited. wrote, sang) at the (concert, competition, airport) because our (ink, flight, effort) was delayed.

32 The (cot. baby, milk) was born in (November, morning, Saturday), a few weeks before (breakfast, bedtime, Christmas).

33 (Remember. Forget, Sorry) to put (bright, small, capital) letters at the (start, middle, end) of each sentence.

34 Let (you, me, those) know what (speed, rate, time) you'll (gone, arrive, came).

35 Hand the (envelope, stamp, pen) containing the ticket (winning, money, concert) to the school (playground, rules, secretary).

Change the first word into the last word by changing one letter at a time and making two new, different words in the middle.

Example TEAK   TEAT   TENT   RENT

36 SALE   _____   _____   MILD

37 HARD   _____   _____   HOLE

38 BOTH   _____   _____   MITE

39 STOP   _____   _____   SEEM

40 WILD   _____   _____   LINK

41 WANT   _____   _____   BARS

42 FILE   _____   _____   FAIL

Find and underline the two words which need to change places for each sentence to make sense.

Example She went to <u>letter</u> the <u>write</u>.

43 The dog scratched it door when the wanted to come in.

44 We like meet you earlier if you can.

45 Saturday grazed his knee playing rugby last he.

46 Did your like you present?

47 Today too cold it's to open the window.

Add one letter to the word in capital letters to make a new word. The meaning of the new word is given in the clue.

Example   PLAN   simple   _plain_

48 CAP   applaud   _____

49 INSET   put in   _____

50 SPRIG   bound   _____

51 SOCK   horrify   _____

52 CUE   remedy   _____

5

Change the first word of the third pair in the same way as the other pairs to give a new word.

Example   bind, hind   bare, hare   but, _hut_

53 raise, ear   night, tin   defer, _____

54 dive, dove   live, love   firm, _____

55 style, let   taper, era   heath, _____

56 swore, row   grate, tar   stone, _____

57 scarf, car   stare, tar   steam, _____

5

Complete the following sentences in the best way by choosing one word from each set of brackets.

Example   Tall is to (tree, <u>short</u>, colour) as narrow is to (thin, white, <u>wide</u>).

58 Rabbit is to (carrot, fur, hutch) as horse is to (hoof, stable, gallop).

59 Stick is to (tree, throw, glue) as start is to (end, commence, leave).

60 Tongue is to (taste, mouth, teeth) as eye is to (glasses, sight, colour).

61 Plunge is to (soar, raid, dip) as monitor is to (computer, disc, track).

62 Bowl is to (cereal, plate, throw) as command is to (boss, ruler, order).

63 Fake is to (money, pretend, genuine) as continuing is to (context, stopping, unchanging).

6

Underline the word in the brackets which goes best with the words given outside the brackets.

Example   word, paragraph, sentence   (pen, cap, <u>letter</u>, top, stop)

64 car, train   (brakes, engine, aeroplane, luggage, road)

65 assemble, gather   (scatter, manufacture, pupils, disperse, collect)

66 parsnip, onion   (vegetable, plum, grow, carrot, cook)

67 difficult, hard   (easy, advantage, contrast, complicated, separate)

68 limit, confine   (extend, vast, restrict, unending, free)

5

Move one letter from the first word and add it to the second word to make two new words.

	Example	hunt	sip	<u>hut</u>	<u>snip</u>
69	blank	air	_____	_____
70	bread	tea	_____	_____
71	splash	soil	_____	_____
72	pray	tack	_____	_____
73	clause	pod	_____	_____

Fill in the crosswords so that all the given words are included. You have been given one letter as a clue in each crossword.

74–75

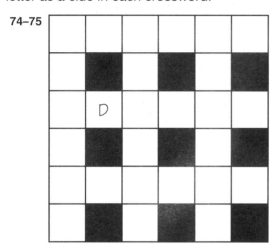

plants, endows, adding, tenors, towers, pleats

76–77

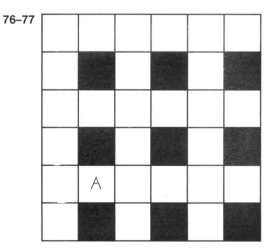

sanity, gyrate, excise, camera, ermine, energy

A, B, C, D and E are cars parked in a straight line. A is not first in the line, but it is in front of at least three cars. B is directly behind C. C is two cars behind D. D is not last in the line.

78 Which car is last in the line? _____

79 How many cars are in front of B? _____

80 Which car is first in the line? _____

81 Are there any cars behind E? _____

82 If D and C swap places, which car is now behind D? _____

Give the missing numbers in the following sequences.

| | **Example** | 2 | 4 | 6 | 8 | <u>10</u> | 12 |

83	27	_ _	46	57	69	82
84	9	20	11	_	13	16
85	25	81	36	64	49	__
86	48	84	42	24	12	_ _
87	93	82	73	66	_ _	58
88	2	10	40	120	_	240

Read the first two statements and then underline one of the four options below that must be true.

89 'Megan goes to school. She has a part-time job.'

Megan does her job every day.

Megan only works at weekends.

Megan can work when she is not in school.

Megan wants to work full time.

Read the first two statements and then underline one of the four options below that must be true.

90 'I need to buy a birthday card. The shop is closed.'

I'm going to a birthday party.

I will have to buy the card tomorrow.

I am unable to buy a card in that shop.

I will make a card myself.

Read the first two statements and then underline one of the four options below that must be true.

91 'A cat is an animal. Animals have legs.'

A cat has fur.

A cat has four legs.

A cat has legs.

A cat has kittens.

Read the first two statements and then underline one of the four options below that must be true.

92 'A boy plays football. Football is a sport.'

       The boy likes football.

       The boy plays for his school team.

       The boy plays sport.

       The boy wears football boots.

Read the first two statements and then underline one of the four options below that must be true.

93 'I write stories. I use an ink pen.'

       I sometimes make mistakes.

       I like using an ink pen.

       Everyone in our class uses an ink pen.

       I write stories with an ink pen.

5

If the code for FRANCHISE is ? × $ £ / + @ ! O, what are the codes for the following words?

B 24

94 FREE   _____   95 SAFE   _____   96 FRESH _ _____

What do these codes stand for?

97 / + O O ! O _____   98 ! + $ × O _____

99 / + @ O ? _____   100 / $! O _____

7

Now go to the Progress Chart to record your score!   **Total** **100**

Paper 8

Underline the two words which are the odd ones out in the following groups of words.

B 4

Example	black	<u>king</u>	purple	green	<u>house</u>
1 sledge	snow	frost		aeroplane	boat
2 bold	hero	fearless		timid	courageous
3 bottle	water	vase		kettle	sieve
4 consist	consent	constant		permit	allow
5 globe	circuit	course		track	footstep

5

Underline the two words, one from each group, which are closest in meaning.

Example (race, shop, <u>start</u>) (finish, <u>begin</u>, end)

6 (famous, unknown, common) (wrote, noted, exciting)

7 (pull, puff, spent) (push, blow, saved)

8 (jagged, sad, jealousy) (smooth, envy, jolly)

9 (count, maths, opposed) (subtract, support, matter)

10 (pupil, teach, study) (confuse, lessons, guide)

B 3

5

Underline the one word in the brackets which will go equally well with both the pairs of words outside the brackets.

B 5

Example rush, attack   cost, fee   (price, hasten, strike, <u>charge</u>, money)

11 thing, article   argue, protest   (oppose, motive, objective, object, item)

12 blaze, heat   shoot, explode   (electrify, inspire, dismiss, sparkle, fire)

13 murmur, sigh   hint, gossip   (breathe, divulge, whisper, whistle, suggestion)

14 cost, amount   consequences, sacrifice   (charge, expense, penalty, outlay, price)

15 pause, stop   destroy, ruin   (rest, shatter, break, demolish, crack)

5

Find the three-letter word which can be added to the letters in capitals to make a new word. The new word will complete the sentence sensibly.

B 22

Example The cat sprang onto the MO.   <u>USE</u>

16 Most children attend a PARY school close to their home. _____

17 She SPED air freshener in the kitchen after frying the onions. _____

18 The ARCECT has drawn the plans for our extension. _____

19 His football shirt has distinctive black and white STES. _____

20 Her father recently started a new job with a different COMY. _____

5

Underline the pair of words most opposite in meaning.

B 9

Example cup, mug   coffee, milk   <u>hot, cold</u>

21 opposite, different   oppose, favour   spray, surge

22 feeble, strong   brilliant, excellent   cram, stuff

43

23 contest, struggle	entire, partial	expended, spent
24 illustrate, represent	plot, conspiracy	invade, evacuate
25 faded, dim	people, folk	failure, success

5

Find two letters which will end the first word and start the second word.

Example   rea (c h) air

26 form   (—— ——)   tract

27 pru   (—— ——)   glect

28 upp   (—— ——)   upt

29 stre   (—— ——)   ount

30 garl   (—— ——)   icle

31 light   (—— ——)   ing

32 bri   (—— ——)   ate

B 10

7

Underline two words, one from each group, that go together to form a new word. The word in the first group always comes first.

Example   (hand, green, for)   (light, house, sure)

33 (plea, sea, left)   (sent, sure, hand)

34 (force, inn, great)   (full, fully, stall)

35 (par, on, con)   (ant, form, down)

36 (set, pick, stir)   (all, ring, tea)

37 (in, tall, stay)   (too, spire, bell)

B 8

5

Find and underline the two words which need to change places for each sentence to make sense.

Example   She went to letter the write.

38 That suits really colour you.

39 I've made with appointment an the optician.

40 We can on my parents collect the way.

41 I sent her this text a morning.

42 She didn't do had as well as she quite expected.

B 17

5

Complete the following expressions by filling in the missing word.

B 15

Example   Pen is to ink as brush is to _paint_.

43 Man is to woman as king is to _____.

44 Before is to earlier as after is to _____.

45 Sweet is to sour as false is to _____.

46 Up is to down as high is to _____.

47 Wood is to solid as water is to _____.

5

Find the four-letter word hidden at the end of one word and the beginning of the next word. The order of the letters may not be changed.

B 21

Example   The children had bats and balls.   _sand_

48 I've taken the drab old curtains down.   _____

49 The gravy was going lumpy in the saucepan.   _____

50 Do you notice how ornate the decorations are?   _____

51 They do drama in the hall.   _____

52 She had been neglecting aspects of her work since it became harder.   _____

5

Remove one letter from the word in capital letters to leave a new word. The meaning of the new word is given in the clue.

B 12

Example   AUNT   an insect   _ant_

53 RESIN   strap to control a horse   _____

54 TITLE   covers roof, floor or walls   _____

55 THREAT   attend to   _____

56 SCORE   painful   _____

57 VARNISH   die out   _____

5

Complete the following sentences by selecting the most sensible word from each group of words given in the brackets. Underline the words selected.

B 14

Example   The (children, books, foxes) carried the (houses, books, steps)
                    home from the (greengrocer, library, factory).

58 The (leaves, stones, plates) turn (blue, sparkly, yellow) every (Autumn, birthday, minute).

59 Hurry (up, down, across)! We (were, will, are) be late for our (choice, place, appointment).

60 He has (already, soon, presently) (chosen, walked, eaten) your (present, mile, hunger).

45

61 We (deliver, bring, introduce) our cat (in, on, below) every (dozen, season, night).

62 Take your (feet, scarf, pen) off the (sofa, hook, shoes) – you'll get (drink, mud, hair) on it.

5

Find a word that can be put in front of each of the following words to make new, compound words.

B 11

Example	CAST	FALL	WARD	POUR	<u>DOWN</u>
63 TIGHT	STRIP	LINE	LOCK	_____
64 SCRIPT	CARD	CODE	MARK	_____
65 PLUG	SHOT	RING	PIECE	_____
66 PIT	REST	LOCK	CHAIR	_____
67 CAME	CROWD	LAP	SEAS	_____

5

Change the first word of the third pair in the same way as the other pairs to give a new word.

B 18

Example	bind, hind	bare, hare	but, <u>hut</u>
68 stern, ten	force, ore	stain, _____
69 weak, awe	real, are	lean, _____
70 rapid, raid	cheat, chat	marsh, _____
71 rough, tough	test, vest	drown, _____
72 mad, dame	elf, flee	sir, _____

5

Fill in the crosswords so that all the given words are included. You have been given one letter as a clue in each crossword.

B 19

73–74

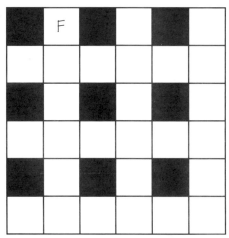

myrtle, meddle, draped, carpet, alkane, flurry

46

hoards, lament, admits, hollow, outcry, diners

Look at the first group of three words. The word in the middle has been made from the other two words. Complete the second group of three words in the same way, making a new word in the middle of the group.

Example	PAIN	INTO	TOOK	ALSO	*SOON*	ONLY
77 CAROL	CARE	PEDAL		SONAR	_____	IDEAL
78 SOIL	LIFE	FEUD		GRID	_____	SHUT
79 SPITE	TRIPS	PRESS		DRUMS	_____	SOLVE
80 LUCK	CLAP	PART		EASY	_____	LATE
81 SIDED	SAID	IDEAS		TAMED	_____	ALARM

Read the first two statements and then underline one of the five options below that must be true.

82 'The girl likes music. Her favourite musical instrument is the piano.'

      The girl plays the piano well.

      The girl likes listening to music.

      Keys on a piano are black and white.

      A piano is a musical instrument.

      The girl can read music.

Read the first two statements and then underline one of the five options below that must be true.

83 'Breakfast is a meal. A meal is an occasion when food is eaten.'

      Most people eat cereals or toast for breakfast.

      Breakfast is eaten in the morning.

      Food is eaten at breakfast.

      Orange juice is a popular drink.

      Breakfast is followed by lunch.

Read the first two statements and then underline one of the five options below that must be true.

84 'Summer is a season. There are four seasons.'

It is hot in summer.
Autumn comes after summer.
Christmas is in the winter.
Summer is one of four seasons.
People go on holiday in the summer.

Read the first two statements and then underline one of the five options below that must be true.

85 'Rain is made of water. Rain falls from the sky.'

Rain makes puddles.
Water comes from rivers.
Snow falls from the sky.
Heavy rain causes floods.
Water falls from the sky.

Poppy and Gertie are dogs. Charlie and Rosie are cats. Gertie and Rosie like tinned food. Charlie and Poppy prefer biscuits. Gertie and Charlie have short hair; Poppy and Rosie have long hair. Only Gertie likes eating bones.

86 Which cat has long hair? _____

87 Which dog doesn't like bones? _____

88 Which dog prefers tinned food? _____

89 Which cat is short-haired and eats biscuits? _____

90 What sort of food does Poppy like? _____

Give the missing pairs of letters in the following sequences. The alphabet has been written out to help you.

A B C D E F G H I J K L M N O P Q R S T U V W X̌ Y Z

	Example	CQ	DQ	EP	FP	*GO*	*HO*
91	CS	EQ	___	IM	KK		___
92	BC	YX	EF	VU	___		___
93	DW	EV	FU	___	___		IR
94	AT	PE	CR	RG	EP		___
95	AZ	___	CX	DW	EV		___

4

B 25

5

B 23

5

the code for DOG is FQI, what are the codes for the following words? The alphabet has
een written out to help you.

A B C D E F G H I J K L M N O P Q R S T U V W X Y Z

5

96 FILM _____   97 DINNER _____   98 SHOES _____

99 TABLE _____ _   100 PAPER _____ ?

Now go to the Progress Chart to record your score!   Total ⭕ 100

Paper 9

$$\frac{95}{100}$$

Underline the two words in each line which are most similar in type or meaning.

B 5

	Example	dear	pleasant	poor	extravagant	expensive
1	aid	city	business	cottage	company	
2	alarm	ignore	greet	advise	disregard	
3	hockey	piano	match	listen	guitar	
4	clear	usual	rinse	distinct	vague	
5	chair	table	wardrobe	crate	stool	

5

Complete the following sentences in the best way by choosing one word from each set
of brackets.

B 15

Example   Tall is to (tree, short, colour) as narrow is to (thin, white, wide).

6 Come is to (appear, leave, due) as fall is to (hurt, asleep, rise).

7 Massive is to (small, elephant, size) as soft is to (pretty, hard, easy).

8 Fair is to (hair, school, just) as faithful is to (believers, devoted, disloyal).

9 Broke is to (ruined, faulty, rich) as familiar is to (family, strange, people).

10 Nest is to (twigs, den, bird) as palace is to (country, queen, luxury).

5

Find the letter which will complete both pairs of words, ending the first word and starting
the second. The same letter must be used for both pairs of words.

B 10

Example   mea (t) able   fi (t) ub

11 fanc (__) oung   tr (__) ard

12 rea (__) ate   hei (__) ock

13 fai (__) ead   curtai (__) ow

14 brai (__) asty   crow (__) ature

15 brin (__) ill   cas (__) ick

16 bre (__) ant   gro (__) hole

6

Find the three-letter word which can be added to the letters in capitals to make a new word. The new word will complete the sentence sensibly.

B 22

Example   The cat sprang onto the MO.   <u>USE</u>

17 The new curtains really BHTEN up the room.   _____

18 The FORY has closed, so lots of people will have to look for new jobs.   _____

19 Put all the clothes back in the WARDE.   _____

20 The garden beside the old COTE was very overgrown.   _____

21 The DRIPG tap kept me awake last night.   _____   **5**

Underline two words, one from each group, that go together to form a new word. The word in the first group always comes first.

B 8

Example   (hand, <u>green</u>, for)   (light, <u>house</u>, sure)

22 (every, ever, never)   (were, less, one)

23 (no, now, some)   (won, all, here)

24 (awe, drop, war)   (rain, rant, full)

25 (cape, leg, skill)   (all, end, able)

26 (in, race, con)   (end, tract, salt)

27 (tab, reason, rise)   (sing, able, up)   **6**

Rearrange the letters in capitals to make a new word. The new word has something to do with the first words.

B 16

Example   spot   soil   SAINT   <u>STAIN</u>

28 ledge for support   flat piece of wood   FLESH   _____

29 lose weight   food   TIDE   _____

30 wild dog   hunts in a pack   FLOW   _____

31 genuine   existing   EARL   _____

32 negotiate   hand out   LEAD   _____   **5**

Find the four-letter word hidden at the end of one word and the beginning of the next word. The order of the letters may not be changed.

B 22

Example   The children had bats and balls.   <u>sand</u>

33 The label lets the consumer read product information.   _____

34 Never open our door to strangers.   _____

35 This area definitely improved when the houses were built.   _____

36 They stored ripe apples in the cellar.   _____

37 His curt acknowledgement of the problem didn't help.   _____   **5**

Complete the following sentences by selecting the most sensible word from each group of words given in the brackets. Underline the words selected.

B 14

Example   The (<u>children</u>, books, foxes) carried the (houses, <u>books</u>, steps) home from the (greengrocer, <u>library</u>, factory).

38 He usually (returns, sees, follows) from work (through, concerning, about) 6 p.m., in time to (put, repair, eat).

39 Three (dogs, drivers, pupils) were (strict, absent, bored) from my class due to (danger, blame, illness).

40 The (train, boat, car) left the (platform, garage, harbour) and headed out to (air, rail, sea).

41 As it's (hot, weak, dim) today, I'll (hit, cross, give) you money for extra (fuel, drink, paper).

42 I don't (frighten, deliver, think) that I have the (right, left, straight) skills for the (job, meal, way).

5

Underline the two words which are the odd ones out in the following groups of words.

B 4

Example   black   <u>king</u>   purple   green   <u>house</u>

43 tennis   cricket   grasshopper   football   net

44 wonder   surprise   trepidation   amazement   concern

45 include   exclude   allow   bar   eliminate

46 catalogue   words   dictionary   address   atlas

47 responsive   wanting   willing   respectful   forthcoming

5

Move one letter from the first word and add it to the second word to make two new words.

B 13

Example   hunt   sip   <u>hut</u>   <u>snip</u>

48 heard   fist   _____   _____

49 beat   gain   _____   _____

50 club   earn   _____   _____

51 leash   fast   _____   _____

52 taint   pint   _____   _____

5

Find and underline the two words which need to change places for each sentence to make sense.

B 17

Example   She went to <u>letter</u> the <u>write</u>.

53 She needed her words to find the dictionary.

54 That the cat and dog sleep in both bed.

55 Go to switch the light off before you remember to bed.

51

56 Put the back in that box.

57 I'll leave a message not you're if there.

5

Underline the two words, one from each group, which are closest in meaning.

B 3

Example　　(race, shop, <u>start</u>)　　(finish, <u>begin</u>, end)

58 (progress, work, cover)　　(attack, advance, change)

59 (eat, graze, playful)　　(scrape, trouble, naughty)

60 (own, separate, live)　　(combine, detach, fix)

61 (coins, money, bank)　　(spend, debt, deposit)

62 (senior, plain, chief)　　(junior, firm, main)

5

Look at the first group of three words. The word in the middle has been made from the other two words. Complete the second group of three words in the same way, making a new word in the middle.

B 18

Example　　PAIN　　INTO　　<u>TO</u>OK　　　ALSO　　<u>SOON</u>　　ONLY

63 DATE　　DIAL　　LILT　　　BLUE　　_____　　VOTE

64 KITE　　STIR　　SPUR　　　VEIN　　_____　　TOUR

65 LITRE　　TRAIL　　TRAWL　　　PUSHY　　_____　　TYRES

66 BEAN　　BINS　　SUIT　　　TIPS　　_____　　SPOT

67 RINSE　　SENSE　　UPSET　　　RUGBY　　_____　　BEGAN

68 POKE　　KEEP　　BEAK　　　TILE　　_____　　HATS

6

Fill in the crosswords so that all the given words are included. You have been given one letter as a clue in each crossword.

B 19

69–70

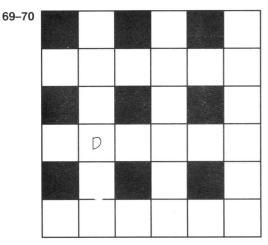

adorns, crusty, puddle, quiver,
averse, celery

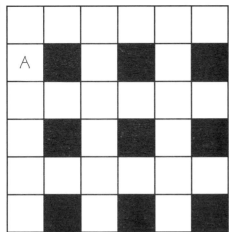

landed, insane, should, oyster,
themes, saints

A, B, C, D and E are five towns. C is due west of B and due north of A. A is east of E and B is due south of D.

73 Which town is north east of C? _____

74 Which town is furthest west? _____

75 How many towns are north of B? _____

76 Which town is south west of C? _____

D

C   B

E   A

Fill in the missing letters. The alphabet has been written out to help you.

A B C D E F G H I J K L M N O P Q R S T U V W X Y Z

Example   AB is to CD as PQ is to RS

77 JS is to IR as ND is to ___

78 KC is to HF as UI is to ___

79 QF is to SH as OB is to ___

80 BM is to GJ as PE is to ___

Underline the wrong number on each line.

Example   3   6   <u>10</u>   12   15

81 16   24   32   43   48   56

82 10   20   31   42   53   64

83 96   84   70   60   48   36

84 66   54   44   36   31   26

85 42   20   35   33   28   30

Read the first two statements and then underline one of the five options below that must be true.

86 'A rose is a plant. Plants grow in soil.'

    Roses are red.

    Roses grow in the garden.

    Rose bushes have thorns.

    Roses grow in soil.

    Rose stems can be put in a vase.

Read the first two statements and then underline one of the five options below that must be true.

87 'Biscuits are food. Food is eaten.'

    People enjoy biscuits with a cup of tea.

    Some biscuits are covered with chocolate.

    Biscuits are eaten.

    Biscuits are stored in a tin.

    Food can be just a snack.

Read the first two statements and then underline one of the five options below that must be true.

88 'A computer is a machine. People design machines.'

    You can play games on a computer.

    Computers are used in schools.

    A computer has a keyboard.

    Some people don't have a computer.

    Computers are designed by people.

Read the first two statements and then underline one of the five options below that must be true.

89 'Kittens are animals. Kittens are small.'

    Kittens drink milk.

    Some kittens scratch.

    Some animals are small.

    Kittens like to play.

    Kittens grow into cats.

Read the first two statements and then underline one of the five options below that must be true.

90 'A grape is a fruit. Wine is made from grapes.'

Fruit is the opposite of vegetable.

Grapes grow on bushes.

People drink wine.

Other fruits can be used to make wine.

Wine is made from fruit.

5

If the code for FRAGILE is IUDJLOH, what are the codes for the following words? The alphabet has been written out to help you.

B 24

A B C D E F G H I J K L M N O P Q R S T U V W X Y Z

91 PLATE _____   92 CHILD _____

93 BOOK _____   94 DESK _____

4

If A = 2, B = 3, C = 4, D = 5, E = 6 and F = 7, find the sum of the following words by adding the letters together.

B 26

95 FADE _____   96 CEDE _____   97 EBB _____

98 FED _____   99 BEEF _____   100 DEAF _____

6

Now go to the Progress Chart to record your score!   Total ( ) 100

Paper 10   97/100

Rearrange the letters in capitals to make another word. The new word has something to do with the first two words.

B 16

	Example	spot	soil	SAINT	STAIN
1	jump		soar	PEAL	_____
2	travel cost		charges	SAFER	_____
3	fraud		deceive	TEACH	_____
4	twist		fasten	CREWS	_____
5	exchange		trade	PAWS	_____

5

Underline the two words, one from each group, which are closest in meaning.

B 3

Example   (race, shop, start)   (finish, begin, end)

6 (grumble, customer, try)   (praise, illness, moan)

7 (reading, play, narrate)   (stage, role, tell)

55

8 (subject, school, future) (matter, history, present)

9 (sow, crop, vegetable) (harvest, sell, increase)

10 (similar, assorted, chocolate) (various, plain, sophisticated)

B 4

Underline the two words which are the odd ones out in the following groups of words.

Example	black	<u>king</u>	purple	green	<u>house</u>
11 gold	jewel		silver	ring	copper
12 elbow	leg		wrist	back	shoulder
13 assess	court		judge	prison	consider
14 Saturn	Mercury		planet	Mars	star
15 stop	discontinue		proceed	continue	persist

B 5

Underline the one word in the brackets which will go equally well with both the pairs of words outside the brackets.

Example rush, attack cost, fee (price, hasten, strike, <u>charge</u>, money)

16 request, plea fascinate, tempt (prayer, charm, interest, appeal, attract)

17 smash, break overpower, overcome (crunch, crush, crusade, grind, cause)

18 jump, leap cellar, tomb (bound, spring, cavern, chamber, vault)

19 growth, advance event, situation (result, outcome, development, expansion, improvement)

20 closing, final continue, remain (stay, fade, latest, extreme, last)

B 22

Find the three-letter word which can be added to the letters in capitals to make a new word. The new word will complete the sentence sensibly.

Example The cat sprang onto the MO. <u>USE</u>

21 They entertained each other with SY stories, but were too frightened to switch off the light! _____

22 She ran straight to the SGS when they arrived at the park. _____

23 He wore his red SWSHIRT to the football match. _____

24 My train was DEED, so I missed the meeting. _____

25 I DEITELY want to see the movie. _____

Find the letter which will complete both pairs of words, ending the first word and starting the second. The same letter must be used for both pairs of words.

Example   mea (t) able   fi (t) ub

26 basi (—) ight   rai (—) eak

27 cas (_ _) ide   boo (—) ale

28 gree (—) ial   len (—) ust

29 poo (—) ice   bea (—) oad

30 cha (_ _) late   soa (_ _) lain

31 par (—) eep   pic (_ _) ilt

6

Find a word that can be put in front of each of the following words to make new, compound words.

Example   CAST   FALL   WARD   POUR   DOWN

32 LEAF   ACT   TIME   WEIGHT   ———

33 FRONT   HILL   HOLD   KEEP   ———

34 WARDS   TASTE   NOON   THOUGHT   ———

35 SURFING   PIPE   SWEPT   SCREEN   ———

36 HOW   TIMES   ONE   BODY   ———

37 COOK   COVER   GO   LINE   ———

6

Complete the following sentences by selecting the most sensible word from each group of words given in the brackets. Underline the words selected.

Example   The (<u>children</u>, books, foxes) carried the (houses, <u>books</u>, steps) home from the (greengrocer, <u>library</u>, factory).

38 I couldn't do my homework (under, because, into) the (kettle, TV, computer) was (fast, new, broken).

39 (Write, remember, study) the list down so you don't (think, avoid, forget) (nothing, something, sometime).

40 The (dentist, office, optician) telephoned to (say, explain, remind) me to collect my (cups, glasses, drinks).

41 Can we (go, leave, depart) to the (cinema, pool, restaurant) for a (chip, pizza, popcorn)?

42 Every (July, March, December), there is an ice rink in our town centre and children (eat, ride, skate) while their parents (shop, dig, swim) for Christmas.

5

Change the first word of the third pair in the same way as the other pairs to give a new word.

Example   bind, hind   bare, hare   but, hut

43 black, back   smack, sack   spent, _____

44 fast, sat   fact, cat   lift, _____

45 board, rob   wound, now   tease, _____

46 loaf, foal   read, dear   meat, _____

47 man, mean   met, meet   bar, _____

Complete the following expressions by filling in the missing word.

Example   Pen is to ink as brush is to paint.

48 Brother is to sister as father is to _____.

49 Hour is to minute as year is to _____.

50 Bitter is to sweet as present is to _____.

51 Two is to double as one is to _____.

52 Daisy is to flower as peach is to _____.

Look at the first group of three words. The word in the middle has been made from the other two words. Complete the second group of three words in the same way, making a new word in the middle.

Example   PAIN   INTO   TOOK   ALSO   SOON   ONLY

53 PEACE   BASE   BRUSH   PROUD   _____   CALLS

54 FABLE   MALT   EMPTY   LIONS   _____   BRAGS

55 CARTON   TRAP   HAMPER   SNATCH   _____   TINKLE

56 FRUIT   THIRD   HANDS   GAMES   _____   THEME

57 COTTON   TORE   FOREST   COFFEE   _____   SLOWER

58 KEEN   KITE   LIST   TEAR   _____   BACK

Move one letter from the first word and add it to the second word to make two new words.

Example   hunt   sip   hut   snip

59 speed   fed   _____   _____

60 mother   end   _____   _____

61 hear   lent   _____   _____

62 long   tow   _____   _____

63 canoe   but   _____   _____

Give the two missing pairs of letters in the following sequences. The alphabet has been written out to help you.

A B C D E F G H I J K L M N O P Q R S T U V W X Y Z

	Example	CQ	DQ	EP	FP	*GO*	*HO*
64	CH	FK	IN	LQ	___	___	
65	KP	MN	OL	___	___	UF	
66	AV	NE	CT	LG	___	___	
67	RF	QG	PH	OI	___	___	
68	AZ	___	CX	DW	___	FU	
69	GH	JK	NO	ST	___	___	
70	TC	UB	WZ	ZW	___	___	

Fill in the crosswords so that all the given words are included. You have been given one letter as a clue in each crossword.

71–72

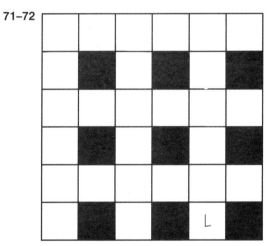

rising, yelled, strike, sprays, result, kennel

73–74

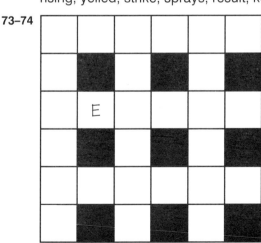

melted, little, eleven, valley, letter, volume

Mark, Chiman, David and Simon all earn weekly pocket money. Mark earns the least, £6 less than Simon. David earns twice as much as Chiman, who earns £1 more than Mark. Simon earns £13 per week.

75 Who earns the most? _____

76 How much does Chiman earn? _____

77 How much does Mark earn? _____

78 How much less than David does Mark earn? _____

79 If David gives Chiman half of his money, how much less than Simon does David now earn? _____   **5**

If the code for CONGRATULATE is ? + ! × − $ @ * O $ @ £, what are the codes for the following words?

C O N G R A T U L A T E (handwritten above code)

80 RATE _____   **81** LATER _____   **82** TEAL _____

What do these codes stand for?

83 @ − £ $ @ _____   **84** − * O £ _____

85 ! £ $ − _____   **86** O $? £ _____   **7**

Read the first two statements and then underline one of the four options below that must be true.

87 'There are pages in the book. There are pictures in the book.'

Each page has a picture.

There is no writing in the book.

The book is for children.

There are some pictures in the book.

Read the first statement and then underline one of the four options below that must be true.

88 'I left a message for my friend.'

My friend was out.

My friend was busy.

I could not speak to my friend.

I sent a text to my friend.

Read the first two statements and then underline one of the four options below that must be true.

89 'I walk my dog every day. My dog doesn't like rain.'

My dog won't go out when it rains.

I take an umbrella when it rains.

Sometimes it's raining when my dog goes out.

I take my dog out when it's stopped raining.

Read the first two statements and then underline one of the four options below that must be true.

90 'Red isn't my favourite colour. Today I am wearing a red sweater.'

I don't like my sweater.

Someone else gave me the sweater.

I hardly ever wear the sweater.

I prefer other colours to red.

If $A = 2$, $B = 3$, $C = 4$, $D = 5$ and $E = 6$, give the answers to these calculations.

91 $B \times C =$ _____

92 $(E + A) \div C =$ _____

93 $(D^2 + B^2) - C^2 =$ _____

94 $B \times (C + D) =$ _____

95 $(2A + 3B) + E^2 =$ _____

A B C D E F G H I J K L M N O P Q R S T U V W X Y Z

96 If the code for REST is TCUR, what is the code for ABOUT? _____

97 If the code for CASTLE is ghfpqr, what is the code for LAST? _____

98 If the code for ENACT is DOZDS, what is the code for SOUP? _____

99 If the code for ADEPT is pctjl, what is the code for PET? _____

100 If the code for BED is YVW, what is the code for DAY? _____

Now go to the Progress Chart to record your score!   Total   100

Progress Chart   Verbal Reasoning 11⁺-12⁺ years Book 2

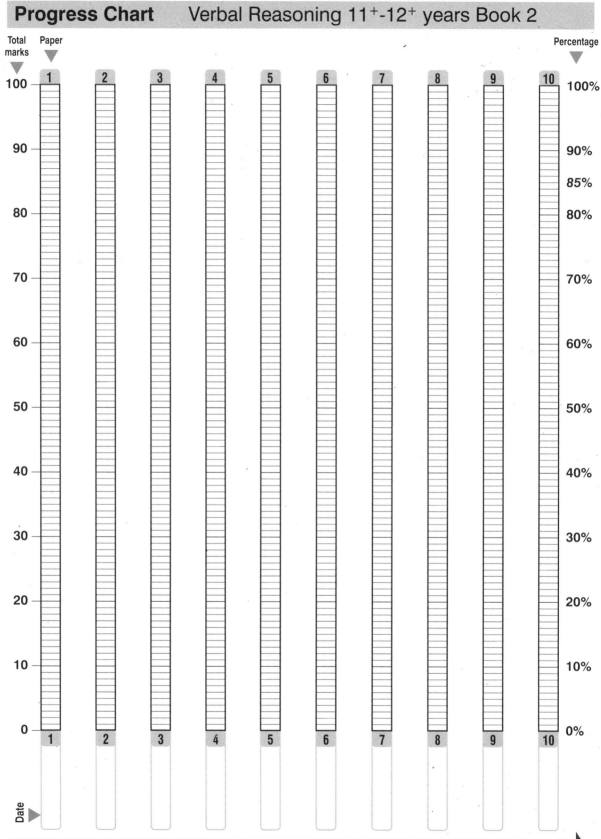

When you've finished the book use the Next Step Planner